Curriculum Motivation Series

A Necessary Dimension in Reading

THE ALMOST GHOST AND OTHER STORIES

Leo C. Fay
Professor of Education
Indiana University

Eth Clifford
Children's Author

 Lyons & Carnahan

An Affiliate of Meredith Publishing Company

CHICAGO   WILKES-BARRE   DALLAS   ATLANTA   PASADENA   PORTLAND

Art Director
R. G. Herrington

Illustrations
Carol Burger

Stories

Ghosts All Around

Thinking Things Over

Ghosts All Around

The Ghosts of the Dark Woods

Once there was a boy who lived with his mother and father. Back of his house stood the Dark Woods. No one ever went into the Dark Woods. No birds sang there. And no animals played under the trees.

One day, the little boy said, "I would like to go into the Dark Woods."

"No, no!" his mother said. "There are things in the Dark Woods that can hurt you. No one knows what these things are. But you must never go there. Never!"

"Do the Dark Woods go on until you come to the end of the world?" asked the boy.

"No one knows what is at the other end of the woods," his mother answered. "But it is said that an enchanted princess lives there. She cannot come out of the Dark Woods until someone helps her."

"Then I must go to the other side of the woods and help her," the little boy said.

"No, no!" his mother said again. "No one who has gone into the Dark Woods has ever come back."

The little boy thought about the Dark Woods. What things lived there? Did they stop the birds from singing? Did they keep the animals from playing under the trees?

Then the boy thought about the princess. Was there a princess at the end of the Dark Woods? Someone would have to go through the Dark Woods to find out.

So the little boy said to himself, "I will go through the Dark Woods. I will try to find the princess. I am not afraid."

The White Shadows

Before the sun came up the next morning, the little boy left his house. He walked along the path that went into the woods. There were no sounds at all.

At first, the little boy saw only trees. He walked on a short way. Then he saw something that looked like a white shadow. It jumped in front of him.

"I am the Ghost of Silence," the shadow cried. "I ate the birds to keep them from singing. And I will eat you, too!" Then the Ghost of Silence came very close to the little boy and danced all around him.

But the little boy said, "I am not a bird. You cannot eat me."

"Ah-e-e, ah-e-e!" the Ghost of Silence screamed. "Run, or you die! Go back!"

"I cannot go back," the little boy said. He was afraid, but he had to try to find the princess.

He walked on. Then he stopped and closed his eyes. When he opened them and looked around again, the Ghost of Silence was gone.

The little boy followed the path. It did not go straight, but it turned this way and that. He had not gone far when another white shadow flew down in front of him.

"I am the Ghost of Fear," the shadow screamed in a high voice. "I ate all the animals in the Dark Woods. And I will eat you, too!"

"I am not an animal of the woods," the little boy said. "You cannot eat me."

"Ah-e-e, ah-e-e!" screamed the Ghost of Fear, flying around the boy. "Run, or you die! Go back! Go back!"

The little boy felt sad and afraid. But he did not want to go back. He wanted to see what was at the end of the Dark Woods.

He walked on a little way. He closed his eyes again. And when he opened them, the Ghost of Fear was gone.

Two New Ghosts

Still, the little boy followed the path. All at once, cold rain fell from the dark sky. Wind pushed at the trees. Lightning hit the path near the little boy. Then, a new ghost flew down from the sky and stood in front of the boy.

"I am the Ghost of Darkness," the shadow screamed. "I took the sun from the sky and ate it. And I will eat you, too!"

The little boy was shaking with fear. Lightning hurt his eyes. But he said, "I am not the sun. You cannot eat me."

"Ah-e-e, ah-e-e!" the Ghost of Darkness screamed. "Run, or you die! Go back!"

"I must go on," said the little boy to the ghost. Lightning hit near his feet. Wind roared through the trees.

But the little boy set off down the path. He closed his eyes. When he opened them, the Ghost of Darkness was gone.

At last, the little boy came to the end of the Dark Woods. There, he saw a small house. In front of the house stood a tall ghost. It was much bigger than the others. The little boy was more afraid than ever.

"I am the last ghost of the Dark Woods," the shadow called out. "I am the Ghost of Enchantment. Stop where you are!"

When the ghost opened its mouth, the air around the little boy became as cold as ice. Snow fell around the boy. "I have enchanted a princess," the ghost said. "And I will enchant you, too!"

The little boy jumped back in fear. But he said, "I am not a princess. You cannot enchant me."

"Ah-e-e, ah-e-e!" screamed the Ghost of Enchantment. "Run, or you die! Go back while there is still time!"

15

"I have come for the princess," said the little boy. "I cannot go back through the Dark Woods without her."

At these words, the Ghost of Enchantment cried out, "What have you done?"

And the ghost turned into bits of snow. Soon, all that was left of the Ghost of Enchantment was a little snow on the ground. The sun came out again. Then, even the snow was gone.

16

At the End of the Woods

The door of the house opened. A beautiful princess came out. She ran up to the little boy. "Oh, please take me home," she said. "The Ghost of Enchantment is gone."

"I will," the little boy answered. "But we will have to go through the enchanted woods. And we must go by the three other ghosts who live in the Dark Woods."

17

"I am afraid to go through those woods,"
the princess said. "But I will try."

The two children started off on the path
through the Dark Woods. As they walked
along, the princess heard something. "What
is that?" she asked with fear.

"Those are the animals of the woods,"
said the little boy, smiling. "They have
come back! They did not die, after all!"

The children stopped and watched the animals run and play. Then they walked on. Soon, the princess heard another sound. "And that? What is that?" she asked.

"Those are birds singing," the little boy answered. "Listen!"

The children stopped and listened to the singing of the birds. The sun was shining on the trees and on the path.

"Who were the other three ghosts?" asked the princess. "Where are they now?"

"They were the Ghost of Silence, the Ghost of Fear and the Ghost of Darkness," the little boy said. "They are gone. The woods are not enchanted now."

How the people laughed and sang when their beautiful princess came back to them!

As for the little boy, he was very happy. He played in the woods day after day from that time on. And he never saw the ghosts of the Dark Woods again.

The Almost Ghost

"I'm not going," Liz said. "I don't want to visit Ghost Town."

Russ looked at his sister. "Why don't you want to go?" he asked.

Just then, Mr. Bell came into the room.

"Liz isn't going to Ghost Town," Russ said to his father. "She must be afraid."

"Afraid of what?" Mr. Bell asked Liz.

"I'm afraid of ghosts," Liz whispered. "Don't ghosts live in ghost towns?"

Russ laughed at his sister. "Do you really think ghosts live in towns?" he asked.

Mr. Bell said, "No one lives in a ghost town, Liz. All the people have gone away. Only buildings are left."

"Oh!" Liz said. She was not afraid of buildings. Only ghosts made her afraid.

Russ said, "Just think, Liz! Ghost Town opens tomorrow. But we can see it today. We will be the first children to go through Ghost Town."

Then Russ turned to his father. "I'm so glad you work for the people who own Ghost Town, Dad," he said.

"I'm glad, too," Mr. Bell answered. "There will be lines of people waiting to see Ghost Town tomorrow. But no one will be there today. You will see how the town looked in the old days before it became a ghost town."

But when she got there, Liz still did not
like Ghost Town. It looked strange to her,
and it was too quiet.

Nothing moved. There were no cars on the
roads that ran through the town. There were
no people on the walks made of wood in front
of the buildings.

Liz thought the quiet town must be hiding
something. She had a feeling that Ghost
Town was waiting for something to happen.

Liz turned around and looked behind her. "This town is haunted!" she said. "I feel as if people are looking at us from all the windows."

Russ looked around, too. "You make it seem haunted, looking behind you all the time like that," he said. "Come on, Liz! Let's keep walking."

A Face in the Window

"No, I don't want to," Liz said. "I know someone is watching us." She looked at the building across the street. It had a big sign in front that said "Park Hotel." All at once, Liz screamed.

"Don't scream like that!" Russ said. "What did you see? There isn't anything strange over there."

"I saw the face of a ghost in the hotel window!" Liz said. "I really did."

Russ said, "There are no ghosts, Liz. You know that." Just the same, Russ looked around. It was very quiet.

"Look up at the window, Russ." This time, Liz was whispering. "I saw the face again!"

Mr. Bell looked at the window. He did not see anything strange from the outside. But he said to Liz and Russ, "Stay here. I want to look inside the hotel."

25

"Wait for me, Dad! I want to help you catch that ghost," Russ called.

"Me, too!" Liz said. "I don't want to stay here alone on a haunted street."

"Come on, then," said Mr. Bell. He walked across the street and into the hotel with the children close behind him.

The Haunted Chair

Mr. Bell called out, "Is anyone here?" He listened, but there was no answer. Then he walked around the quiet room. At last, he said, "I still don't see anything strange."

Then Liz jumped. "Look there!" she said in a whisper. "I see something strange, all right. That chair is moving!"

Russ said, "I wish you would stop seeing things, Liz!" But when he looked at the chair, he saw something strange, too. The chair really was rocking—and no one was sitting in it!

"The chair is still moving!" said Liz. "I told you there really were ghosts! One of them is sitting there, watching us!"

Russ turned to his father and said, "Dad, chairs don't rock without people in them."

"It must be the wind," Mr. Bell answered.

"But there is no wind inside," whispered Russ. He went over to the rocking chair and put his hand on the seat. "This seat is still warm," he said. "Something has been sitting here, and it just left!"

"This place is full of ghosts," Liz said. "I told you Ghost Town is where all the ghosts live!"

"Don't be silly, Liz," Mr. Bell said. "A ghost couldn't make a chair warm."

"I'm going outside," Liz shouted. As she ran out, she looked up the stairs. "Look at that door at the top of the stairs," she said. "It's closing, and no one is there!"

30

Mr. Bell and Russ looked up the stairs, too. As they watched, the door closed with a soft noise.

"A ghost couldn't close a door, and we know this hotel isn't haunted," Mr. Bell said. "So something else is making these things happen."

"Dad is right," Russ whispered to Liz. "A ghost really couldn't close a door."

"Wait here," Mr. Bell told Liz and Russ. He went up the stairs, opened the closed door and went inside. Then the children heard him say, "Who are you? What are you doing here? Come on out!"

"He has your ghost, Liz," Russ said. "There comes the ghost now!"

The Talking Ghost

An old man came out of the room. As he came down the stairs, he said, "I didn't think anyone would visit here today." Then he sat down in the rocking chair and began to rock.

"I didn't mean to make you afraid," he said. "But I used to live in this town when I was a boy. It was called Silver Hill then, and it was a busy place."

"You used to live in this ghost town?" Russ asked, surprised.

The old man laughed. "Silver Hill was a real town when I lived in it. You see, back then, people were looking for gold in this part of the country. They didn't find much gold, but they did find silver. There was a big mine here, and Silver Hill became a large town."

"What happened to the mine?" Russ asked. "We still need silver, don't we?"

"The silver we use for money and other things comes from other places now," the old man said. "Men took all the silver out of the ground here. When there was no more silver, the mine closed and people left. Then Silver Hill became a ghost town."

"Oh, Dad!" Russ said. "Could he show us around Ghost Town—I mean Silver Hill?" Russ asked.

"That would be fun," said Liz. Ghost Town didn't seem haunted to Liz now. But she liked the name Silver Hill better.

Mr. Bell laughed. "Well," he said, "this man knows more about the town than I do. I only helped to make the town look as it did in the old days. He lived here when it was still a town, before the people left."

"Follow me," the old man said. "I want to show you the old mine."

As he walked along, the old man said, "The mine isn't far from here. Weeds and grass have about covered the door that goes down into the side of a hill. The mine has been closed for years now, but you can see where silver was mined then. . . ."

"Isn't this fun?" Liz whispered to Russ. "I'm glad we came."

"But you were the one who didn't want to come here," Russ said with surprise. "You thought you would find a ghost!"

"Well," answered Liz, "I almost found one, didn't I?"

Thinking Things Over

The Lucky Ball Game

"Come on, Avery!" Lon called from the front steps of Avery's house. "We don't want to miss the start of the ball game."

Avery came out of his house, but he didn't seem to be in a hurry. "They can't start the game without us," he said.

"They might," Lon answered. "But you are the star pitcher, and they couldn't win the game without you. So come on, Avery! It's a long walk to the ball park from here."

At last, Avery was ready to go. The two boys walked as fast as they could down the sidewalk. While they walked, Avery threw a penny up and down, up and down.

"Don't do that!" Lon said. "You might drop your penny. Then we would have to hunt for it. We are late enough as it is."

Just then, the penny fell on the sidewalk. But it didn't roll far away. It stopped under a ladder, which was standing on the sidewalk near a window.

"I see the penny!" Lon said. "It's under that ladder. Hurry, hurry, Avery!"

But Avery just looked at the ladder. Then he looked at the penny. "It's my lucky penny," he said, "and I can't pitch a ball game without it."

Lon said, "Let's get it, then, so we can go on."

"Oh, no!" Avery answered. "It's bad luck to walk under a ladder. I have to think of another way to get my penny without going under the ladder."

"Oh, boy!" Lon said. He ran to the ladder, picked up the penny and gave it to Avery. "Please put this in your pocket before you drop it again," he said.

"I can't lose my lucky penny. We can't win the game without it," Avery answered.

"If we win the game, it will be because you are the best pitcher," Lon said. "That penny can't win the game without you."

A Long Way to Go

The two boys walked on as fast as they could. But before they had gone very far, Avery stopped walking again.

"Now what?" Lon asked.

"You made me hurry so much that I left my bat at home," Avery said.

42

"You can use my bat," Lon answered. "But come on, will you?"

"No, I can't use your bat. That would be bad luck," Avery said.

Lon was getting cross with Avery. "Well, run back and get your own bat, then."

"But I can't go back," Avery said. "It's bad luck to go back for something that you have left behind."

"Is it all right if I run back and get the bat?" Lon asked. "I don't care if it's bad luck or not. I don't believe pennies and things can bring good or bad luck. I just want to get to the ball game today!"

Lon ran all the way to Avery's house. While he ran, he talked to himself. "That Avery!" he said. "I never saw anything like it! Everything is bad luck. It's a wonder he can get through the day!"

Lon found Avery's bat on the front steps. He picked it up and ran back.

Avery saw Lon coming. "You found the bat!" he called. "Now I know our team will win the game today!"

"Sure, sure," Lon answered. He looked at Avery. "Tell me something," he said. "Do you think the boys on the other team believe in good and bad luck?"

"Sure they do," Avery said. He looked at Lon in surprise.

"Do you think they might have good luck things like your lucky penny?" Lon asked.

"Sure they do," Avery said again.

"Well, let's say the other pitcher has a lucky penny, and you have a lucky penny," Lon said. "How can you both be lucky? One pitcher will win and one will lose. The pennies can't bring good luck to you both."

A Bad Luck Cat

But Avery was not listening to his friend. While Lon was talking, a black cat ran in front of the boys.

"Did you see that?" Avery said. "It was a black cat! We can't cross his path! We will have to go some other way."

"There isn't any other way to go," Lon said. "And we are so late now that the game may have started without us."

Avery said, "You know that Lee is the only other pitcher we have. And he has never pitched a full game. The team will just have to wait for us."

Lon answered, "But they have to start the game on time, Avery. You know that."

Still Avery didn't move. "You saw the black cat cross our path," he said.

Lon felt cross again. "I don't care if you want to believe all these silly things. But you are not the only boy on the team. If we lose, will you say that a black cat lost the game for us?" Lon asked.

"There is nothing I can do about it," Avery said.

"Your lucky penny and your lucky bat are two good luck things. And there was only one cat," Lon pointed out. "Why don't we go on and see what happens?"

"All right," Avery said at last. He and Lon ran. Avery looked around a few times, but he didn't turn back.

It's up to Avery

When the two friends got to the ball park, they saw that the boys on their team were not happy.

"Where have you been?" one boy shouted. "Lee had to pitch. The other team already has four runs. And it's still the first inning! What a game! Help us out, Avery!"

They waved Lee in from the mound and sent Avery out to pitch.

There were two outs. If only Avery could strike out the next batter!

"Good luck!" Lee called to Avery.

"Please!" Lon said. "I don't want to hear that one more time today!"

But Avery didn't hear Lee. He was already out on the field, warming up to pitch.

Then Avery stepped up to the mound to pitch. When he was ready, he threw the ball to the batter. It was a good pitch.

The batter tried to hit the ball.

"Strike one!" the umpire called.

Avery threw the ball again. This time, he threw a fast pitch. The boy tried to swing at the ball, but it was too fast.

"Strike two!" the umpire shouted.

Avery threw another fast ball. Still the boy could not hit the ball.

"Strike three!" said the umpire.

The boy was out, and the inning was over.

Avery pitched a fine game that day. The other team got only two hits while he pitched, and no home runs came in. Avery's team won the game, 5 to 4.

All the team came over to Avery. They patted him on the back. "Good going," one boy said. "We thought we would lose."

"I know why we won," Lon said. He looked at Avery and laughed. "We won because a black cat ran in front of us. And a black cat is good luck, you know."

"No, no. It's the other way around," Avery began. "A black cat is bad luck. . . ."

Avery stopped talking, because he saw that Lon was smiling at him. "Oh, I don't know," he said. "You may be right, Lon. I guess a black cat is good luck. Something helped us win the game."

"We have a good pitcher and a good team," Lon said. "That is why we won."

"All the same," Avery answered, "I'm still glad I had my good luck penny!"

My Name Is Miguel

One afternoon, Mr. Diaz said, "Miguel, will you help me before you go outside?"

"Please, Father! Don't call me Miguel!" Miguel said.

"But that is your name," said Mr. Diaz, surprised.

"But it's not my name. Miguel is a Spanish word. My name is Mike," the boy answered.

"Mike?" Mr. Diaz asked. "Is Mike better than Miguel, my son?"

"Yes, it's a better name," Miguel said. "In this country, boys don't have strange names like Miguel. People laugh at me when I tell them my name. So please, Father, I want to be called Mike from now on."

"I see," Mr. Diaz said. He looked away from his son. He knew that Miguel felt sad because he didn't like his name.

Mr. Diaz also knew there were other things that Miguel didn't like about his family. For one thing, Miguel didn't want his father and mother to speak to him in Spanish when his friends were visiting.

"Don't talk in Spanish," Miguel had said one night. "Speak English. My friends don't know Spanish, and they don't know what you are saying. Their fathers and mothers speak English, and my friends laugh when they hear you talk in Spanish."

"Why should they laugh?" Mr. Diaz asked.

"Because Spanish is different," Miguel answered. "That is why."

"Is it so bad to be different?" Mr. Diaz wanted to know.

"Yes, Father," Miguel answered. "It's very bad to be different. I want to be like all my friends."

"Why?" Mr. Diaz asked again.

"I just do," said Miguel. He felt cross because he didn't know why he couldn't give his father an answer. "And it's not only that you speak Spanish," he went on. "But you also go to school. I thought that schools were made for children."

"But I go to learn! Is it not a good thing to learn, my son?" Mr. Diaz asked.

"It's not that," the boy said. "You are not a child. You are too old to go to school."

Mr. Diaz answered, "I do not go to your
class in the morning. I go to a class at night.
All the people there are big now. But our
teacher does not think we are too old to go
to school. She is glad that we all want to
learn. That is why she comes to night school
to help us."

"But she has to teach you," Miguel said,
still cross. "She is a teacher."

58

Mr. Diaz felt sad. "My son," he said, "go out and play. I will do my work alone."

Miguel ran out of the house. He was glad to go. He didn't stop to think that his father was sad. He liked to get away from the house. There, he was always Miguel. Outside, he was someone else. He was Mike.

"Thank You, George."

Sometimes, Miguel had homework to do when he came home from school. Once in a while, his friend George came home with him. Then the two boys did their homework together. And sometimes, Miguel went to George's house to do his homework.

When Miguel went to George's house, he always looked around. How different George's house looked inside! George's parents didn't wear the same kind of clothes. The food they ate was different. And his parents always talked in English.

Miguel thought that everything different must be better. He liked to go to George's house, but he didn't like for George to come home with him.

Mr. Diaz often had homework to do, too. One afternoon, Mr. Diaz was at home when

Miguel and George came in. He was sitting
at the big table in the kitchen, and he had a
lot of papers in front of him.

"My friend and I have homework to do,
Father," Miguel said. "We need that table
for our papers." He wished that his father
would go out of the room.

But Mr. Diaz moved some of his homework
out of the way and said, "Here. Now there
is room for all."

"No, no," Miguel said. "You can't work
here, Father. We talk while we do our work,
and you couldn't get your homework done."

"Oh, we can be quiet, Mike," George said.

The two boys started their homework. Then George saw that Mr. Diaz did not know how to do some of his work. "Can I help you with something?" George asked.

"My father does not need your help," Miguel said. He didn't want George to see what his father was doing.

"Thank you, George," Mr. Diaz said. "I do need your help. I do not know this word."

George looked at the book Mr. Diaz was holding. "That word is 'bubble.' It's a hard word to read." Then George said, "Are you coming to our school tonight, Mr. Diaz?"

Mr. Diaz looked surprised. "Why should I go to your school tonight?" he asked.

"All the parents will be there tonight. Our school is having an open house so the parents can talk to the teachers. Didn't Mike tell you about tonight?"

Miguel didn't look at his father when he said, "I didn't tell him."

Mr. Diaz saw that Miguel didn't want him to visit the school. He also saw that Miguel didn't want the teacher to meet his parents.

Mr. Diaz said to George, "Miguel's mother has been sick this week with a bad cold. But I will come to the school tonight." Mr. Diaz didn't say anything to Miguel.

Mr. Diaz Goes to School

That night, Mr. Diaz told Miguel, "You do not have to go with me. I can go alone."

Miguel answered, "The teacher and the class will know you are my father. So I might as well go, too."

All the lights were on when Mr. Diaz and Miguel came into the school building. Many people were walking in and out of different classrooms. They were talking and laughing, and all the parents seemed to be having a good time.

Miguel took his father to his classroom. He went over to his teacher and said, "Miss Winters, I would like you to meet my father. My mother couldn't come tonight."

"Hello, Mr. Diaz," Miss Winters said in a happy voice. "I'm so glad to meet you. I want to meet Mrs. Diaz, too, when she can come visit here." She smiled at Miguel. "I hope you and your father can stay after the others go home. I want your father to help me with something."

Miguel looked surprised. "How could my father help you?" he asked.

"Me?" Mr. Diaz said at the same time. "You are a teacher. I am the one learning."

Miss Winters laughed. "I go to a Spanish class," she said. "I'm trying to learn to speak Spanish, but it's very hard for me."

"I didn't know teachers went to school," Miguel said.

"Oh, yes, Miguel," Miss Winters answered. "Teachers go to school to learn more. We want to learn new things, too." She looked at Mr. Diaz. "Spanish is beautiful! But I need help with some of the words. Could you help me, Mr. Diaz?"

"I will be glad to do what I can," Mr. Diaz answered.

Miguel couldn't believe what he had heard. Did Miss Winters really need his father's help? Then he said out loud, "Did you say that Spanish is beautiful?"

"Why, yes. Anyone would say that Spanish is beautiful," Miss Winters said. "I want to go to Mexico this summer. But I have to learn more Spanish before summer comes."

Miss Winters turned to Mr. Diaz. "I can't speak Spanish the way you do," she said. "And I think you will laugh at the way I speak. But, with your help, maybe I can speak it well enough to go to Mexico."

Mr. Diaz smiled. "I will not laugh at your Spanish if you will not laugh at my English," he said.

Miss Winters smiled, too. She said, "Thank you, *amigo*."

Mr. Diaz was pleased. "I see you know the word for friend!" he said.

Then Miss Winters saw that other parents were waiting to talk to her. As she turned away, she said, "Thank you again, *amigo*."

"Think of that!" Miguel said. "My teacher wants to learn Spanish! And she is as old as you are, Father! But still she wants to learn more."

Just then, George came over to Mr. Diaz. "I want you to meet my father," he said.

"Is that all right with you, Miguel—I mean Mike?" Mr. Diaz asked.

"Sure, *amigo!*" Miguel said. Then he said, "You don't have to call me Mike."

"But I thought you said that Mike was a better name," Mr. Diaz said.

The boy smiled at his father. "My name is Miguel," he said.

The Present

"Why do we have to move?" Alec asked his mother. "When we moved here, you said we wouldn't have to move again."

"Yes, I remember," Mrs. Brothers said. Then she tried to tell Alec why the family had to move. "Your father went to school at night to learn new things," she said.

"And now he has new work in Stonefield, where we are moving." Mrs. Brothers smiled at Alec. "He found a nice house there, too."

"We live in a nice house now," Alec said.

"Our house in Stonefield will be much better," Mrs. Brothers said. "And you can play in the park there. I don't like for you to play in the street, as you do here."

74

Alec went to the window and looked out. The houses stood in a long row, and they all looked the same. There were no trees or flowers in front of any of the houses. But Alec didn't really see those things. He was thinking about something else.

"This street looks fine to me," he said. "And besides, all my friends live here."

Mrs. Brothers said, "You will make new friends in Stonefield, Alec. It's fun to meet different people."

"It may be fun for you," Alec answered. "But I like the friends I have."

Mrs. Brothers said, "Why don't you say good-by to your friend Ralph now? Then you can come back and help me pack."

Alec ran out of the house. He remembered what had happened when he first moved to this street. The other boys his age wouldn't play with him. They didn't seem to want to make a new friend.

Alec used to watch the other boys playing. They didn't look at Alec, and when he tried to talk to them, they walked away.

But one day, Mr. Brothers brought home a baseball mitt for Alec. None of the boys Alec's age had a baseball mitt. That same day, Alec came out of his house and sat down on the front steps. He put his mitt on one hand and hit it with the other hand.

Soon, one of the boys came over to him. "Is that baseball mitt yours?" he asked.

Alec said, "Dad gave it to me. Would you like to try it out?"

The other boy smiled. "Come on and play with us," he said. Then he said, "I wish I had a baseball mitt like yours."

Soon, that boy became Alec's best friend. His name was Ralph. Now he wouldn't be Alec's best friend any more.

"Good-by, Alec!"

Alec walked down the street. The older boys were playing ball, and Ralph was watching them. The older boys wouldn't let Ralph or Alec play with them. They said the small boys were too little to play ball. But if the big boys needed someone else, they let Ralph play.

"Have you played yet?" Alec asked, when he came up to Ralph.

"No, not yet," Ralph answered. "But Buddy has to go home soon. His mother just called him. Then they will ask me to play. Just wait and see."

"I know," Alec answered.

"When are you moving?" asked Ralph.

"First thing tomorrow morning," Alec said.
He didn't know why he felt so sad. But he
wished Ralph wouldn't play with the older
boys this afternoon. He wished Ralph could
go home with him and help him pack.

"It's too bad you have to move. You are
my best friend," Ralph said. "I wish I had
a good-by present for you, Alec. But I don't
have enough money to buy a present."

"It's all right," Alec answered. "I don't really care." But the more he thought about it, the more Alec thought a good-by present would be nice. For one thing, it would make him feel better about moving.

Just then, one of the older boys in the street stopped playing. Another boy called to him, "Come on, Buddy! You don't have to go home right now! The game isn't over!"

But Buddy said, "Let Ralph play in my place." He walked away and didn't look back to see what happened.

Ralph looked at Alec and smiled. "See? I told you I would get to play before the day was over," Ralph said. He was glad, because he loved to play baseball with the older boys. It made him feel older, too.

Alec said, "I'm going home, too. My mother wants me to help her pack. I guess I will have to say good-by now, because the movers are coming early in the morning." Alec waited for Ralph to say something.

Then one of the big boys called to Ralph again. "Come on, if you want to play!"

"Sure thing!" Ralph called back. As he ran out to play, he looked back over his shoulder at Alec. "Good-by, Alec!" he called. Then he saw Alec's face and stopped.

"Well, what are you waiting for?" the big boy called once more.

Ralph turned to the boy and said, "Play without me today. I can't play baseball with you, after all."

The older boy was surprised. "Why can't you play?" he asked. "Listen, boy, if you don't play when we tell you to, you can't play ball with us again. Understand?"

Ralph answered, "I don't want to play. Alec is my best friend, and he feels sad about moving away tomorrow."

"So?" the big boy said. "What about it?"

"I don't have a present for him," Ralph answered. "So this is my good-by present."

"I don't see a present," the older boy said, still surprised.

But Ralph and Alec were already walking down the street, away from the big boy.

The big boy looked after them. "How is not playing with us a good-by present?" he asked another boy. He didn't understand.

But Alec did. "Thank you, Ralph," he said. "Presents make people feel better. And having a good friend like you is the best present anyone ever gave me."

Little Eagle's Adventures

The Wild Horse

Little Eagle lay on the hill and looked out across the valley. He lay as still as he could, and he didn't make a sound. But he never stopped watching something that was moving slowly across the valley floor.

For a long time, Little Eagle waited, hiding behind the tall grass which grew on the hill. At last, he could see that the small, moving spots down in the valley were two men. But the men were not on foot. They were riding on something!

86

Little Eagle moved slowly away from his hiding place. Then he ran to the village.

He went straight to his father, who was the chief of the Indian people. "Two men are coming to our village!" he said. "But they do not walk. They sit on big animals! What wonderful, big animals they are!"

No one in the village had ever seen big
animals that men could ride. All Indians
walked then, even when they hunted big
buffaloes or left their villages.

When the men rode into the village on
their strange animals, all the people ran out
to see them. But they were afraid at first.
They had never seen men with pale faces
before, and they had never seen such
animals as these. They did not even know
what the men called their animals.

Little Eagle's father, who was called Many Feathers, went up to the white men.

The men with pale faces got off their animals. One of the men came closer to Many Feathers. "We rode as fast as we could on our horses," he said. "But it took us many days to find your village."

Many Feathers put out his hands and patted one of the three spotted animals. He saw that this horse was tied to one of the others by a long rope. He wondered why the men had brought this horse with them. "Why do you come?" he asked the men.

"We know that your people have many buffalo hides," the man said. "We need hides, and we want to trade for them."

Many Feathers looked at the horses. "Yes, we can trade. We will give you many buffalo hides for your wonderful animals," he said.

"Oh, we couldn't give you our horses!" one of the men said. "We need them. Our home is far away, and we can't walk."

"Many Feathers and all his people walk. We even walk when we hunt," the Indian chief said. "And you do not need three horses. You can ride only two."

90

"No," the white man said. "We may need that horse, too." He opened a bag he had with him. He took strings of colored beads from the bag. "See?" he asked. "We will trade these beads for your buffalo hides."

The people moved closer to the men so they could see the beads. They thought the beads were beautiful. "Yes, yes," they said. "We want to trade. We like the beads."

So Many Feathers did as his people asked. He gave the men buffalo hides, and they gave his people many strings of beads. Then the white men rode away on their horses.

But Little Eagle felt sad. He didn't want beads. He wanted one of the big animals that the men with pale faces owned. Every day, he thought about the strange animals the men had called horses.

Little Eagle's Secret

Then, when Little Eagle was out hunting rabbits, he saw something. He saw a horse racing through the valley. No one was on the horse's back. Who owned the animal? Had he found a wild horse?

Little Eagle gave a loud call, but the horse raced away. "You are afraid now because you are wild," he said. "But you will be a tame horse someday!"

After that, Little Eagle went to the hill every morning. But he didn't tell anyone about the horse down in the valley. He even kept his secret from his father. He wanted to surprise everyone in the village.

When he went to the hill, Little Eagle always took corn for his horse. First, he put corn on the ground. Then he hid in the tall grass and watched the horse nibble at the corn. But one morning, Little Eagle stayed down in the valley.

When the horse came to nibble at the corn, he looked at the Indian boy. But he didn't seem to be afraid now.

Little Eagle talked softly to the horse. "Your name shall be Running Wind," he said. "And you must know the sound of my voice. Running Wind, I am your friend."

When the horse heard Little Eagle, he ran away. But the boy said, "You will not always run away, Running Wind."

As he watched the horse race down the valley, Little Eagle thought, "Someday I will ride on your back, Running Wind. I will ride the way the white men rode." He laughed to himself when he thought how surprised the people of the village would be when they saw him riding Running Wind. How proud Many Feathers would be!

Early the next morning, Many Feathers called his son. "Each day, you go out to hunt," he said. "But the hunter brings back nothing from the hunt. Are there no rabbits? Did all the birds fly away?"

Little Eagle didn't look at his father. He looked down at the ground.

"Did the birds fly away with your voice as well?" Many Feathers asked.

Now, Little Eagle looked up. "I do not hunt rabbits or birds," he said. "But I cannot tell you what I hunt."

Many Feathers was not happy with his son's answer. "You must learn to be a good hunter," he said. "Soon, it will be time for my people to hunt the buffalo."

Time to Hunt the Buffalo

Little Eagle didn't know what to say. A buffalo hunt! All the people would leave the village, taking their things with them. They would follow the buffaloes until they had enough buffalo meat and hides to last for a long time. Then the people would go back to the village.

The Indian boy had always loved to go on a buffalo hunt. But now he couldn't leave Running Wind. So he said to his father, "I am not ready to go now."

Many Feathers was surprised, but he was not pleased. "Does the son tell the father when to hunt?" he asked. "Go, now!"

Little Eagle ran. He knew he had not said the right thing. But he couldn't tell Many Feathers his secret yet. In his hurry, he didn't take corn to Running Wind. When he came to the hill, he threw himself down and waited for the horse.

98

Soon, Running Wind came racing across the valley. He stopped and looked for his corn. He looked up when he heard Little Eagle coming down the hill into the valley.

"You must not run away! Remember, I am your friend!" Little Eagle said.

Running Wind pawed the ground. But when Little Eagle came closer, the horse stood still. The boy put his hand out, and the horse didn't try to run away. Little Eagle talked softly to Running Wind.

The horse seemed to like the sound of Little Eagle's voice. He put his head down and began to nibble at the grass.

"Now I try to ride my horse," Little Eagle said. He jumped up and tried to sit on Running Wind's back. At first, the horse jumped so much that Little Eagle couldn't stay on his back.

But each day, the boy talked softly to his horse while he gave him food. "Running Wind will have much corn," he whispered. "And I will take you to the buffalo hunt."

Soon, Little Eagle rode Running Wind for a short way. The horse didn't seem to care if someone sat on his back or not.

Then Little Eagle wanted to ride fast. He gave his horse a soft tap. Running Wind began to run. How surprised Little Eagle was when he fell off the horse's back! How hard it was to ride a horse!

But little by little, the Indian boy learned to ride Running Wind. He learned how to move with the horse so he wouldn't fall. And at last, he could race with the horse, no matter how fast he ran.

Little Eagle smiled. He was very proud of himself. He had tamed a wild horse! Now his father would be pleased with him!

Another Secret

Little Eagle knew that the people were getting ready for the buffalo hunt. He said to himself, "I can tell my secret now."

It was time for Little Eagle to go to the village. It was time to show his secret to everyone. Little Eagle patted Running Wind, and they rode into the village.

The people looked up when they heard so much noise. "Look at Little Eagle!" one of them called. "He rides the big horse!"

Just then, Many Feathers saw his son on
the horse. How surprised he was!

Little Eagle rode up to his father and got
off the horse. He said, "Little Eagle and
his horse Running Wind are ready for the
buffalo hunt now."

Many Feathers asked, "Is this what Little
Eagle was hunting each morning?"

"Yes," answered Little Eagle.

Many Feathers stepped closer to Running Wind. He ran his hand along Running Wind's back. The horse rubbed Many Feathers' hand with his nose. "And you say you tamed this horse?" Many Feathers asked. "It is hard to tame a wild animal."

"Yes, it was hard work," Little Eagle answered. "But I tamed him." Once again, he felt proud of himself.

104

Many Feathers smiled. Then he talked softly to Little Eagle so the people of the village couldn't hear his words. "You should have told me your secret, Little Eagle. You could have saved much time. Now I have a secret to tell you."

Little Eagle was surprised. "Many Feathers has a secret, too?" he asked.

"I have seen this wonderful animal before, Little Eagle. See the brown on his tail and the white spot on his nose? I first saw him when the men with pale faces came. He was the horse no one rode."

"Then he was not wild?" Little Eagle asked. "Running Wind was already tame?"

Many Feathers said, "I do not think the white men rode him much. So you helped tame him, Little Eagle. You showed him you were his friend."

Then Little Eagle thought of something else. "Will the men with pale faces want him back?" he asked slowly.

"The white men would have looked for him. They would have asked about him if they wanted him back," Many Feathers said. "No, he is your horse now."

Then Many Feathers and Little Eagle turned back to Running Wind and the people of the village. Many Feathers said, "Little Eagle is a good hunter. And some day, Little Eagle will be a great chief."

Two Buffalo Hunts

The time for the buffalo hunt had come.
It was summer, and the buffalo were fat.
For Many Feathers' people, it was the most
exciting time of the year. And now, the
Indian tribe had Little Eagle's horse to help
them hunt buffaloes.

Little Eagle didn't think he could wait.
He had never been so excited.

At last, Many Feathers made a sign. Soon, the braves would leave the village. They would try to find the buffalo herds. The older men of the tribe would stay behind with the women and children.

But first, there would be a buffalo dance. The Indian braves always danced the night before a buffalo hunt.

110

Last Year's Hunt

Little Eagle thought back to last year's buffalo dance. He remembered it very well.

Only the braves who had shot buffalo took part. Some of the braves carried arrows in their hands while they danced. Some carried round sticks. These dancers made a kind of music by hitting the sticks together.

The women of the village never danced. But they sang songs in time with the sticks to help the braves dance better.

All the braves painted their faces with bright colors, as if they were going to war. They thought these strange faces and the dancing would bring good luck to the tribe. They thought their Indian gods would like the dance and would help the braves find a large buffalo herd.

Many Feathers started the dance. He put on the horns and tail of a buffalo, and he painted his face yellow, white and red. Even Little Eagle didn't know him!

The women and the children of the tribe sat in a ring around the dancers. Little Eagle and the other boys liked to watch the dancers and listen to the music. Someday, they hoped to be buffalo dancers, too.

On the morning after the dance, all the braves left the village. Then Little Eagle and his mother, Honey Bee, began to pack.

112

Honey Bee and Little Eagle called their dog. Then they rolled up their tepee made of buffalo hides. Next, Honey Bee tied the tepee across the ends of two poles.

Little Eagle's work was to tie the other ends of the poles to the dog's sides. When the boy finished, the dog could pull the tepee on the poles. The Indians didn't have to carry their tepees.

At the Camp

When Little Eagle and Honey Bee got to
the camping grounds, they took the tepee
off the dog's back. Then they set the tepee
up on the poles.

Little Eagle and the other boys his age
did not go on the buffalo hunt. They had
to stay close to the camp with the women.
They hunted small animals near the camp
so the tribe would have something to eat.

One day, Little Eagle wanted to be big. He wanted to hunt buffalo, too. So he said to himself, "I am not hunting rabbits today. I am going to follow the braves."

Little Eagle thought he was walking very softly. Then he heard a noise that sounded like a bear! Little Eagle was afraid until he saw Many Feathers behind him. Then he knew that his father had made the sound.

"So!" Many Feathers said. "You want to be a hunter! Then you have much to learn!"

"You were in the valley. I was on the hill," the boy said. "How did you see me?"

"A hunter must move without making any noise," Many Feathers said. "I could hear you moving. A bear would have run away."

Little Eagle looked down. He thought his father would send him back to the camp.

But Many Feathers said, "You have come this far. You may go along with us. But you must follow me and do as I do."

Many Feathers walked fast, but he moved without making a sound. Little Eagle went behind him. When Many Feathers moved fast, Little Eagle moved fast. When Many Feathers stopped, Little Eagle stopped.

Many Feathers and his son walked a long way. Then it was time to sleep. And in the morning, Little Eagle saw something that he had never seen before.

Far away, Little Eagle saw a buffalo herd eating grass. Near the buffalo herd was a cliff. But the big animals did not know that Many Feathers and his braves were watching them.

Many Feathers said, "Little Eagle, you are not old enough to hunt big buffaloes. But you may try your arrows on a calf."

Then Many Feathers took the arrows Little Eagle carried. He made a deep cut in each arrow. Now, the Indian braves could tell which arrows belonged to Little Eagle.

Then Many Feathers said, "Watch!" He set fire to the grass. The wind blew the smoke from the fire to the buffaloes.

Soon, the buffalo herd smelled the smoke and saw the fire. The buffaloes began to run, but they couldn't see where they were going. Many ran straight to the cliff.

The arrows of Many Feathers and the braves shot through the air. Then Little Eagle saw a buffalo calf running with the herd. He shot his arrow, too. The calf fell! Little Eagle had shot his first buffalo!

When Many Feathers went down the cliff, he found many buffaloes that had been killed by the fall. Now there would be enough meat for a long time. The tribe would have many hides to make clothes for the winter.

How the Indian braves danced that night! And how they talked about the great hunt!

One of the braves talked about Little Eagle! He said Little Eagle was a good buffalo hunter. Little Eagle liked what the brave said. He felt very proud.

Then Many Feathers said, "You have done well, my son. Today, you shot a buffalo. But you still have things to learn before you become a brave. Remember my words!"

Little Eagle said, "I will remember." But he was very sure that someday he would be a great hunter like his father.

Yes, Little Eagle remembered everything about that first buffalo hunt. But now, it would be a much better hunt. After all, he had Running Wind to help him hunt.

"Who knows?" he thought. "Maybe I can kill a big buffalo this time!" He smiled. It was an exciting thought.

Animals from Far Away

Olav Follows the Reindeer

Olav lived far, far to the north, in the country called Lapland. And Olav was very glad that it was spring, at last!

In Lapland, spring did not bring pretty flowers. The grass did not turn a bright, beautiful green. The trees did not put out any new green leaves.

When Olav and his sisters looked outside, they still saw ice and deep snow. It would not melt for a long time yet. They saw a few small birch trees. And they saw the houses in their village.

The houses were all made of logs, with roofs of birch bark. All the roofs were covered with pieces of sod, for sod helped to keep warm air inside the houses.

The children saw something else, too. They saw the pine forest nearby. And they saw many tracks in the snow. These were the tracks of the reindeer.

All winter, the reindeer lived in the pine forest. There, they didn't feel the snow and cold winds so much. And there grew the moss on which the reindeer lived.

All winter, they had to hunt for moss. Even if the moss was three feet under the snow, the reindeer could smell it. Then they had to dig through the deep snow with their big, hard hoofs.

By the end of the winter, there was not enough moss left in the forest to feed the herds. The reindeer needed fresh feeding grounds. They seemed to know that it was time, then, to leave the forest and go to the high ground. There, the snow melted first, and they could find fresh moss.

And this was why Olav was glad spring had come. For when the reindeer moved, most of the village moved with them. Only the very old people stayed in the village, to take care of the goats and cows.

What busy days these were! There were so many things to take—tents, tools, clothes, food and cooking pots! All the things had to be packed into sleds. Each family had a big, light sled that could be pulled by a reindeer. They looked more like boats than sleds. They would hold many things, but soon the sleds were packed full!

Then Olav and his father had to catch one of their reindeer to pull their sled. One reindeer had been trained to work in harness, but the animal was not very tame. When it was not harnessed to the sled, it stayed with the herds in the forest.

Olav and his father went out to the pine forest. They both had thin lassos made of reindeer hide. Olav's father knew each one of his animals. He pointed out the big, old reindeer that had been trained to pull the family's sled.

Olav got his lasso ready. Then he sent it flying through the air. "I caught him!" Olav shouted. Sure enough, his lasso was caught around the reindeer's antlers.

"Good!" said Olav's father. "Now you can help me harness him."

The animal was not very big. He stood about four feet high at the shoulders. But he was strong. He could pull the sled over snow, even though the sled was heavy.

Off for the High Ground!

The village men who herded the reindeer had dogs to help them. Now they started herds moving to the high ground. The dogs ran nearby, keeping the animals in line.

This spring day was very cold! Olav was glad that he had put fresh hay in his fur boots. The hay kept his feet warm and dry.

At last, Olav's family got into the sled. Their reindeer followed hoof tracks of the herds, off for the high ground. There, the herds would stay until the snow melted.

When they got there, Olav helped carry food, pots, clothes and tools into a sod house. It was made of birch logs and sod, and it looked like a small mound. Inside, it was quite dark, but it was warm.

Olav liked the sod house. But he knew they wouldn't stay there long. For, in the summer, the reindeer would move again.

As summer came to Lapland, snow and ice melted away. All at once, flowers grew up, and leaves showed on the birch trees. But then came insects! The insects flew about, buzzing, and bit people and animals.

The reindeer could stand cold winters, but they couldn't stand insects! Then the herds moved up to the high mountains. The air was too cool there for insects to live, and the moss was fresh and green. All the people followed the reindeer. In the high mountains, the men set up long birch poles and put up their tents. Here they would camp until fall, when the first snows came.

In the summer, all the men took turns at watching the herds. Olav helped his father watch. And, every day, Olav had to find birch sticks to keep fires going. Working in the mountain air made Olav very hungry.

There was good food to eat at the summer camp. And most of it came from reindeer! There was the wonderful cheese that Olav's mother made from the reindeer milk. They used some milk in their hot coffee, too.

And from reindeer meat, his mother cooked wonderful stew in the big cooking pot.

"What would we do if we didn't have the reindeer?" Olav once asked his father.

His father laughed. "But we do have the reindeer," he said. "We have always had them. We couldn't live without reindeer."

"Yes, I know," Olav answered. "Most of our food comes from them."

"Everything we have comes from them," Olav's father said. "Look at our coats."

"They are made from reindeer skins," Olav said. "So are our boots. And so are some of the tents."

"Our harnesses and lassos are made of reindeer hide, too," Olav's father said.

"And you use even their antlers! You can make tools out of them. The reindeer is a wonderful animal!" Olav said, laughing.

Olav liked the summer very much. This was the time of year when the reindeer had their calves. What a little thing a new calf was! It was so small that it had a hard time just standing up! Yet soon, the calf was strong enough to run after its mother.

Olav loved the calves. But his father wouldn't let him pet them. When the calves were bigger, they would have to stay with the herds. But if they smelled of people, the other reindeer wouldn't let them come into the herds. Reindeer could never be really tame animals.

But his father was glad for Olav to stay nearby and talk to the calves. Reindeer that were used to the sound of men's voices could be trained better, after they grew up. Reindeer that would be harnessed had to know the sound of men's voices.

Olav was careful about watching the new calves. Sometimes, a wolf came and tried to kill the little calves.

In the summer, Olav helped his father mark their new calves. Each man who owned a herd had to cut his mark in the ears of his reindeer. Each herd had a different mark. That way, the Lapland men could tell which reindeer belonged to them.

Before Olav knew it, summer was over. The days began to grow short and cold. It rained often. Then snow began to fall, and ice covered the mountain lakes.

Down from the Mountains

With snow, reindeer could pull the sleds back to the village. So Olav's mother began to pack clothes, tools and pots into their sled. Soon, they were ready to leave.

The herds of reindeer went first, with some of the men and dogs to watch them. Then came the other people, riding in sleds or on the backs of reindeer.

Olav's father said that Olav was now old enough to ride a reindeer. But what a hard ride it turned out to be! Riding a reindeer was not like riding a horse.

Olav couldn't make the animal go where he wanted. The reindeer picked its own path, and Olav just had to stick on. The animal went very fast, jumping over rocks, racing across ice and around birch trees.

Olav had been glad in the spring to go away from the village. But how glad he was to see it again, now that fall had come!

But work was not over yet. There was still much to do before winter came.

First, the men drove the herds into one big pen. Then each man had to find his own reindeer and drive them into a small pen.

In the big pen, the reindeer acted wild. They ran every which way. Often, they got into fights. They tried to strike others with their antlers or hoofs. The men and boys shouted at them. Then all the dogs ran about nearby, barking.

Olav looked for the mark of his father's herd. When he saw one of their animals, he threw his lasso. Each time he caught one reindeer by its antlers, his father pulled it away to their own pen. Olav ran behind, shouting and waving his arms.

By night, Olav's father had all of his
reindeer shut in his pen. Soon, he would let
most of them go to the pine forest. From
the others would come food for the winter.
From their skins, Olav's mother would sew
new clothes. His sisters would help with the
sewing of coats and boots.

Olav's father would trade other skins for
things in town. This year, he wanted to
surprise Olav's mother. He was going to get
her a sewing machine! It was a new kind
of sewing machine, that could sew even the
heavy reindeer hides.

138

Now, winter was coming. It was time for Olav and his sisters to go back to school. Until spring, the children would be busy with their books.

When spring came again, once more the reindeer would leave the pine forest and go to the high ground. Then they would move on up to the mountains. The people would follow the reindeer.

And once more, Olav would be glad that it was spring in Lapland, at last.

The Strangest Animal

Glen, Wally and Tony went to a movie, one afternoon. It was about a man who hunted wild animals, all over the world, and then brought them back alive.

The next day, the boys talked about the movie. Glen and Wally had liked it very much. But Tony said, "I thought that was a silly movie. Why does that hunter go so far away, just to catch those animals? Who wants them alive?"

140

Wally looked at him. "Oh, boy!" Wally said. "Tony, you don't know anything! How do you think animals get into zoos? Someone has to catch them!"

"That is what I'm going to do, when I grow up," Glen said. "I'm going to be a hunter. Just like the man in the movie."

"Not me," said Wally. "I want to work in a big zoo, like our city zoo."

Tony began to laugh.

"What is so funny?" Wally asked.

Tony was still laughing. "You, working in a zoo!" he said. "You just want to go around all day, giving animals food?"

"That shows how much you know about a zoo," Wally said. "There is more to taking care of animals than just feeding them."

"Like what?" Tony asked.

"Let's go to the zoo today," Glen said. "Then Wally can tell us about it while we look at the animals."

So the three boys went to the zoo. First
of all, they went to see the lions. The lions
were kept in a big place, with high stone
walls all around it.

"Look at those lions move!" Tony said.
"Some of them are going to break out of
this zoo, someday!"

"No," Wally said, "they can't jump high
enough to get over those walls. But you
can't keep leopards outside, that way."

"Why not?" Glen asked.

"Leopards are wonderful at climbing and jumping," Wally said. "The leopards could jump right out of there. That is why they have to be kept in strong cages."

So the boys went to see the leopards. The leopards walked around and around in their cages. Sometimes, they stopped and looked at the people watching them. The leopards' eyes were mean.

"They look like big cats," Glen said. "Only not so ready to make friends."

"They belong to the cat family," Wally answered. "But you wouldn't want to pet a leopard! They are meat-eating animals!"

Tony said, "That was a silly thing to say." When Glen and Wally looked at him in surprise, Tony said, "Wally said they are meat-eating animals. All animals eat meat!"

"Come with me," Wally said. "I can show you some animals that never eat meat."

They walked a little way. Then they came to a great, flat yard with a fence around it. Inside were some very big animals.

"Oh!" Glen said. "The elephants!"

"They are not meat-eating," Wally said. "And there are many other animals that eat only plants. Deer eat only plants, too. So do all the monkeys."

"Monkeys eat bananas," Tony said.

Wally looked at Tony. "Well, fruit like bananas comes from plants," Wally said.

Glen was watching the elephants. He said, "They sure are big!"

"I know all about elephants," Tony said. "The biggest animals in the world!"

"They are the biggest animals on land," Wally said. "Whales are really the biggest animals in the world. But whales live in the sea, in very deep water."

"I like elephants," Glen said. "When I grow up and start hunting wild animals for zoos, I will catch lots of elephants alive."

"I will be working in a zoo, then," said Wally. "We may not need elephants. We will need more of the real strange animals."

"Like what?" Tony asked.

"Oh, like the new animal the zoo just got," Wally said. "It is the strangest animal here. Come and see it."

He took the boys to another part of the zoo. He stopped in front of a cage. "Good! It isn't in its hole," Wally said. "There! What do you think of it?"

Tony and Glen looked at the animal. They looked up at the sign on the cage. It said: DUCKBILL OR DUCK-BILLED PLATYPUS. Then the boys looked at the animal again.

Tony said, "It's sure funny-looking! But why do you call it the strangest animal?"

Wally said, "In some ways, it's like one kind of animal. In other ways, it's like different kinds. It can swim under water. It stays in a river most of the time. But it digs a hole near the river for its home."

He went on, "Just look at it! It has a big, flat bill, like a duck's. But its bill is soft. A duck's bill is hard. Its feet are a lot like a duck's, but it has claws, too. The platypus digs with those claws. And it has no feathers, as a duck has. It has soft fur, like a beaver!"

Glen said, "I guess it looks more like a beaver than anything else. That tail looks almost like a beaver's tail. It's wide and flat, but there is fur on it. A beaver does not have fur on its tail."

"Well, is it a beaver?" asked Tony. "Or is it some kind of duck?"

Wally said, "What do you think? There is something else—it hatched from an egg."

"If a platypus lays eggs, then it must be a bird," Tony said.

"No, it isn't," Wally answered. "A bird has feathers and two feet. But a duckbill, or platypus, has fur, and it has four feet. It lays eggs, but so do turtles and so do some snakes. Platypus eggs have soft shells, like a turtle's eggs."

"This duckbill thing does not look a bit like a turtle or a snake," Tony said.

150

"But the platypus can fight with poison, as some snakes can. Only the poison does not come from its mouth. The poison is in those long claws by its back feet. It strikes out with the claws, and the poison kills."

Glen was too surprised to answer.

Tony shouted, "Is it a beaver? Or a bird? Or a snake? No! It's a duckbill!"

Glen was thinking. He said, "It does not look like a turtle. But I believe it acts like turtles. What does the platypus eat?"

Wally said, "A baby platypus lives on milk, after it hatches out of the egg."

"Milk!" said Glen. "Baby turtles and birds don't drink milk!"

"But when it grows up," Wally said, "it eats worms. Almost a thousand, every day!"

"Worms!" Tony said. "I wouldn't want to be a platypus. It would be better to be a monkey, and eat bananas. Tell me more about this silly platypus."

"Well, it stays in water most of the time, looking for food," Wally began.

"So do ducks," Glen said. "Quack! Quack! I am a duck-billed platypus!"

Wally laughed. "But it never quacks! It makes a sound more like a growl," he said.

"Quack, quack! Glen, you are a duck!" Tony cried. "Growl, growl, growl! I am a duck-billed platypus!" He looked again at

the strangest animal. "Why don't they get more of them? Why do they have only one, here at the zoo?" he asked.

"It's hard to keep them alive in zoos," Wally answered. "This is the only platypus now alive in this country."

Learning about Animals

"How did you learn so much about animals like this platypus?" Tony asked.

Glen said, "Oh, Wally reads about animals all the time."

"I like animals, and I like to read. I can find out a lot about animals by reading books," Wally said. "I come to the zoo a lot, too. The men who feed the animals tell me things. Sometimes, they let me go into the hospital. I can watch them take care of the sick animals in the hospital."

"You mean they have a hospital here, just for sick animals?" Tony asked in surprise.

154

Wally looked at him. "Don't you think animals ever get sick?" he asked. "Once, I even saw them give a lion a shot with a big needle. They thought he had a cold."

"A needle! Poor lion!" said Tony. "How do they know when an animal is sick?"

"They have animal doctors here," Wally said. "The doctors look over each animal from time to time. They have a lot to do."

"Doctors and hospitals!" Tony said. "I used to think a zoo was just animals shut up in cages."

"The zoo people have to give each animal the right kind of food," Wally said. "And they must make sure each animal has the right kind of place to live in. That means they have to know everything there is to know about animals, to keep them alive."

"Like what?" asked Tony.

Wally asked, "Have you seen the penguins in their pool? They need ice-cold water to swim in. That is what they were used to, in the seas where they were caught. So were the white bears that lived near the north pole. Monkeys need things to climb and to swing on. Each animal needs something different."

"Let's look at some more animals," Tony said. "I want to hear more about some of the other animals. This is fun."

"Well!" Glen said. He laughed. "Now you know why Wally and I liked that movie."

"I want to see that movie again," Tony said. "This time, I know I will like it."

The Almost Ghost, and Other Stories is the third book in the Curriculum Motivation Series. In this book, 91 new words and 43 attack words are introduced. The attack words are selected on the basis of the reading skills of children at this stage of their development and can be derived independently through the use of initial consonant substitution or through the combining of known words to form compound words. Variety in sentence structure and contractions provide natural language patterns consistent with children's oral language.

The readability level of *The Almost Ghost, and Other Stories* is 2.46.

WORD LIST

New Words	*Attack Words*	*New Words*	*Attack Words*
GHOSTS ALL AROUND		22. really	Dad (had)
5. ghosts	. . .	23. strange	. . .
		24. haunted hotel	. . .
6. . . .	. . .	25. . . .	. . .
7. enchanted princess	. . .	26. . . .	. . .
8. through shadows	. . .	27. . . .	. . .
9. silence	. . .	28. . . .	. . .
10. screamed	die (lie)	29. . . .	. . .
11. . . .	fear (near)	30. stairs	couldn't
12. . . .	. . .	31. . . .	. . .
13. lightning darkness	. . .	32. silver	mean (clean)
14. enchantment	. . .	33. . . .	mine (fine)
15. . . .	. . .	34. . . .	. . .
16. . . .	. . .	35. . . .	. . .
17. . . .	. . .	36. . . .	. . .
18. . . .	. . .		
19. . . .	. . .	**THINKING THINGS OVER**	
20. . . .	. . .	37. . . .	. . .
21. whispered	I'm isn't	38. lucky	can't
		39. pitcher penny	sidewalk

158

New Words	Attack Words	New Words	Attack Words
40. ladder	. . .	75. . . .	. . .

41. pitch
    lose
	luck (duck)	76. baseball
		    mitt
			pack (back)
			age (cage)

42. . . .	bat (hat)	77. . . .	. . .
43. . . .	. . .	78. older	. . .
44. team	. . .	79. . . .	. . .
45. . . .	. . .	80. . . .	. . .
46. . . .	. . .	81. . . .	. . .
47. . . .	. . .	82. . . .	understand
48. . . .	. . .	83. . . .	. . .
49. inning	. . .	84. . . .	. . .
50. strike batter	mound (found)		
51. umpire	. . .	**LITTLE EAGLE'S**	
52. won	. . .	**ADVENTURES**	
53. . . .	. . .	85. eagle	. . .
54. . . .	. . .		
		86. valley slowly	. . .

55. Spanish
    son
	. . .	87. village
		    wonderful
			. . .

56. speak
    English
	. . .	88. buffalo
		    pale
			tame (name)

57. different	. . .	89. closer	. . .
58. class	. . .	90. . . .	trade (made)
59. . . .	. . .	91. . . .	beads (reads)
60. parents	homework	92. secret	. . .
61. . . .	. . .	93. nibble	. . .
62. . . .	. . .	94. softly	. . .
63. . . .	. . .	95. . . .	proud (loud)
64. . . .	tonight	96. hunter	. . .
65. . . .	. . .	97. . . .	. . .
66. . . .	classrooms	98. . . .	. . .
67. . . .	. . .	99. . . .	. . .
68. . . .	. . .	100. . . .	. . .
69. Mexico	. . .	101. . . .	. . .
70. amigo	. . .	102. . . .	. . .
71. . . .	. . .	103. . . .	. . .
72. . . .	. . .	104. . . .	. . .
		105. . . .	. . .
73. remember	wouldn't	106. . . .	. . .
74. . . .	. . .		

New Words	Attack Words		New Words	Attack Words
107. . . .	. . .		130. insects mountains	. . .
108. . . .	. . .		131. cheese coffee	. . .
			132. . . .	stew (few)
109. exciting tribe	. . .		133. calves	. . .
110. herds women	braves (saves)		134. . . .	mark (park)
111. dancers	shot (lot)		135. . . .	. . .
112. . . .	. . .		136. . . .	pen (hen)
113. tepee	poles (holes)		137. . . .	. . .
114. camp	. . .		138. sew machine	. . .
115. . . .	. . .		139. . . .	. . .
116. . . .	. . .			
117. cliff	. . .		140. strangest movie alive	. . .
118. . . .	. . .		141. . . .	. . .
119. . . .	. . .		142. . . .	. . .
120. . . .	. . .		143. leopards	. . .
			144. . . .	. . .

ANIMALS FROM FAR AWAY

New Words	Attack Words		New Words	Attack Words
121. . . .	. . .		145. . . .	flat (hat)
			146. bananas biggest	whales (pales)
122. reindeer Lapland	. . .		147. . . .	. . .
123. birch sod	melt (felt)		148. platypus	duckbill
124. forest moss	pine (fine) nearby tracks (backs)		149. beaver	claws (paws)
			150. . . .	. . .
125. . . .	hoofs (roofs)		151. poison	. . .
126. harness	tools (pools) pots (lots)		152. growl	quack (back)
			153. . . .	. . .
127. lassos antlers	. . .		154. hospital	. . .
			155. needle doctors	. . .
128. . . .	boots (roots)		156. . . .	. . .
129. . . .	. . .		157. . . .	. . .

160